INCURABLY MAD!

by Sergio Aragones

Edited by Albert B. Feldstein

WARNER BOOKS

A Warner Communications Company

WARNER BOOKS EDITION

This Warner Books Edition is published by arrangement with E.C. Publications, Inc.

Warner Books, Inc., 75 Rockefeller Plaza, New York, N.Y. 10019

A Warner Communications Company

Printed in the United States of America

10 9 8 7 6

To Nick Meglin

①

②

3

1
2
POOF!

3

1
2

3

L & N
97145

①

2

FOR SALE
FOR SALE
FOR SALE
FOR SALE
FOR SALE
FOR SALE
FOR SALE
FOR SALE
FOR SALE
FOR SALE
FOR SALE
FOR SALE
FOR SALE
FOR SALE
FOR SALE
FOR SALE
FOR SALE
FOR SALE
FOR SALE

SPLAT!

3
SPLAT!

SCENE
IV

1
2
THUNK!

3

①

②

(3)

MARIA

1
2

3

THE GUILLOTINE UNFAIR TO EXECUTIONERS
DOWN WITH AUTOMATION

1
2

3

(1)

2

PET
SHOP

1

2

(3)

1
SLAP

2
WACK!

MATERNI

1

2

3

1
2

3

1

2

3

ROLLER COASTER MFG. CO.

1
2

3

(1)

(2)

3

①

2

HOT

1
2

3
ZZZZ

1
2

3

1

2

3

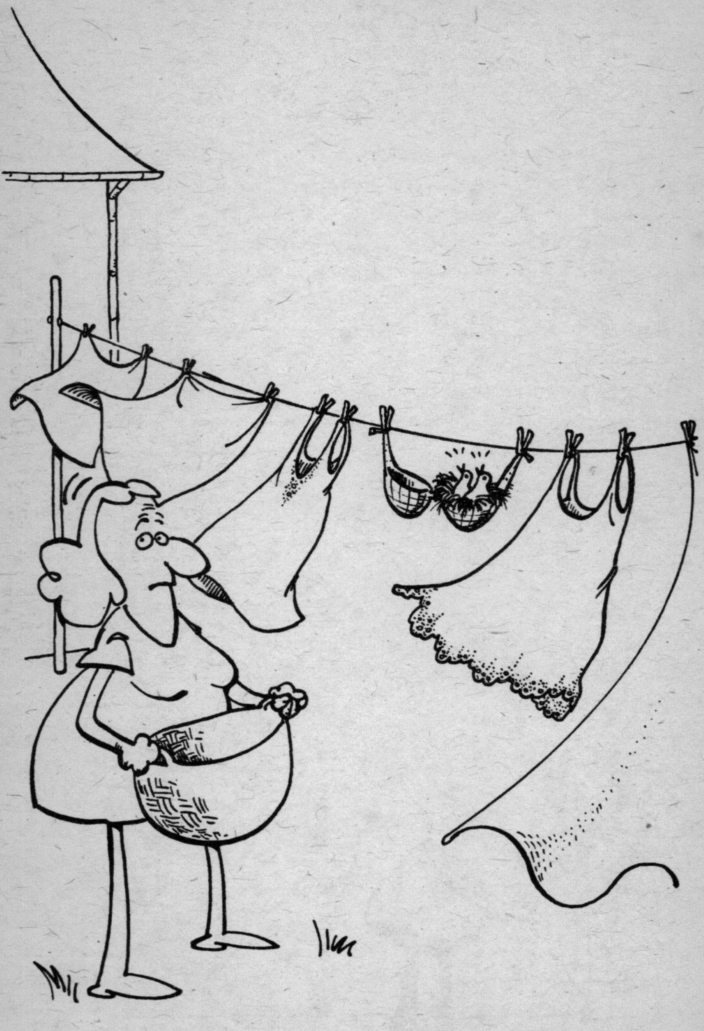

1

2

3
BIRD
WATCHERS

①

2

MUSEUM

3
WACK!!
WACK!!
MARTINIS
25¢

1

2

3

(1)

1
TV
TV

2
TV

1

2

3

1

2

3

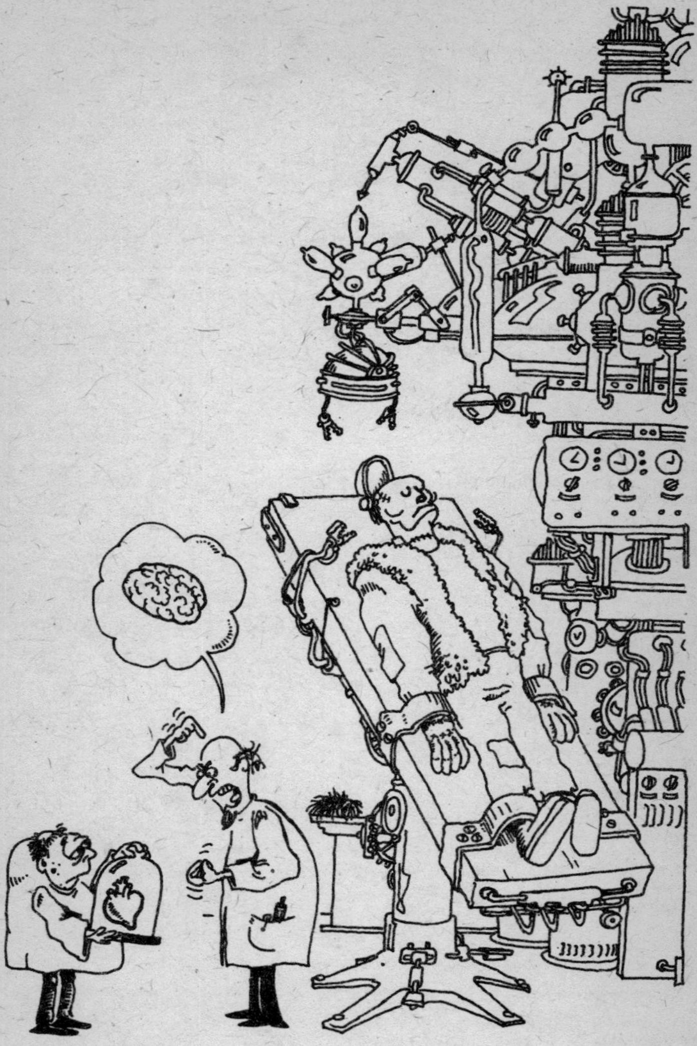

1

2

3

3

1

②

1

2

VACANCY

1

(2)

1

2

NEW SITE
DE LUXE
TOWERS

1
JUST
MARRIED
2
JUST
MARRIED

3

1

2

FRUIT OF THE LOOM

703
201

①

②

3

1

2

3

4

ACUPUNCTURE
針刺

③

1
2

3

BIG
RACE
START

1

②

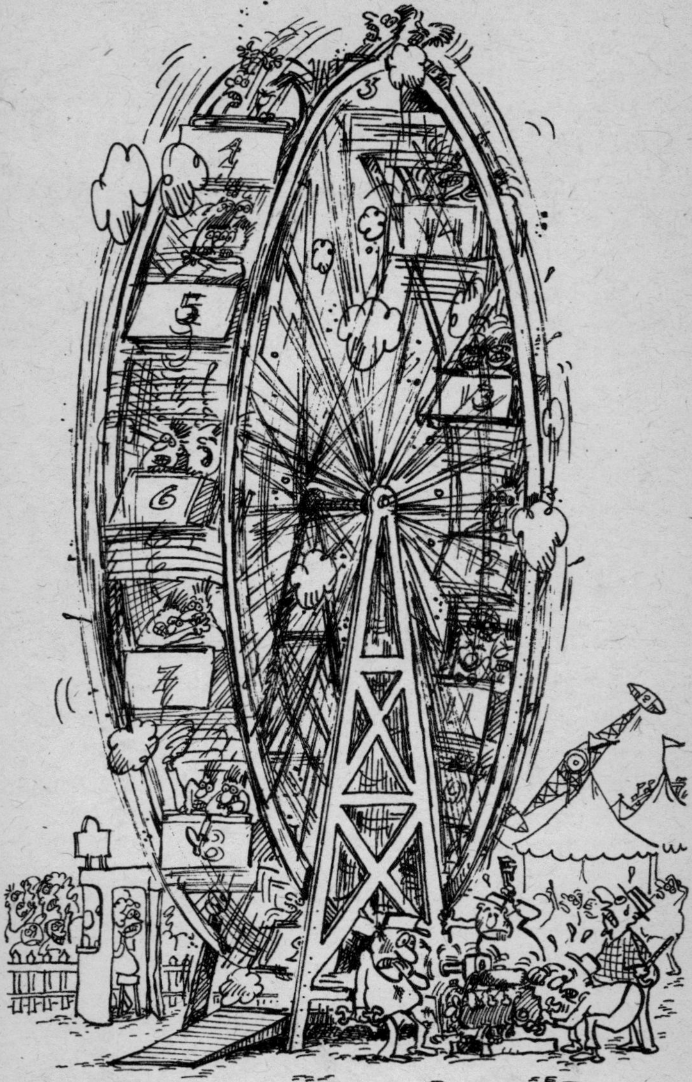
4
5
6
7

1
2

3

①

②

3
PIRANHA

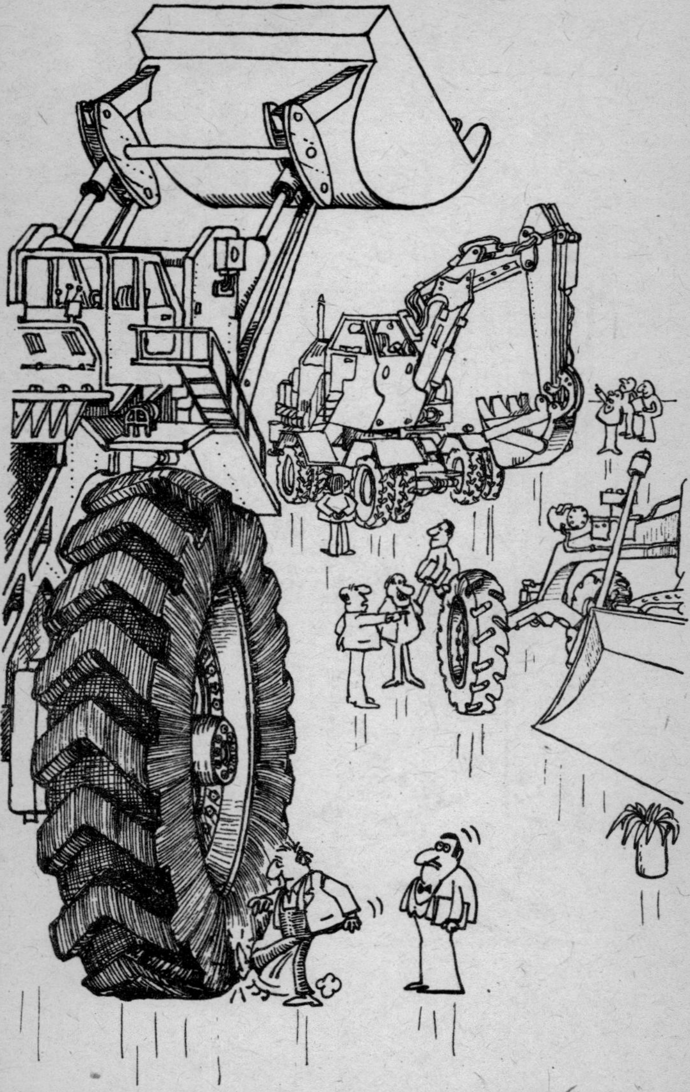

1

2

1

2

3

1

②

SALVATION
ARMY

1
2

3

MAIL

1

2

JOE'S
DINETTE
LAROUSSE
GASTRONOMIQUE

1
GARAGE
JUST MARRIED
LOVE
2
JUST MARRIED
LOVE

3

1

2

1

2

3

3

ARAGONÉS 76
THE END

MORE **MAD** HUMOR FROM WARNER BOOKS